Words to help you...

global   flatter   people   regional   number   population   distribution
sun   densely populated   rain   climate   habitable   good

1 What is Population?

- **Population** is the .... of .... living in a **place**.

2 Distribution

- .... is the spread of **where** people live.

- This can be ...., ... or **local**.

3 Lots of People

Places with **lots** of people, (.................. ....), usually have .... **environments**.

This means they are .... to live in:

- .... land

- good .... with mixture of .... and ....

Western Europe

Eastern USA

Japan

4   **Habitable Environment: River Valleys**

Areas which are easy to get to and have good .... have larger

....

River .... are good
places to live because they
are:

• ....

• have a fresh ....

• have good .... links

• have good ....

Examples:

Rhine Valley, Germany

Ganges Valley, India

5   **Habitable Environments: Lowland Plains**

Lowland .... have:

• ...., fertile ....

• good .... land

• good ....

Examples:

Cereal Farming,
East Anglia (UK)

Dairy Farming,
Denmark

6 **Habitable Environments: Good Natural Resources**

Places with lots of .... also have lots of ....

The UAE (United Arab Emirates) has lots of:

• .... fuel (............., ..., ...)

• materials for ....

• natural .... (............. ore, bauxite).

This makes it a very .... place to live.

7 **Habitable Environments: Coastal Plains**

Coastal Plains are highly
.... because
they have:

• moderate ....

• good .... access

• ....

Examples:

Many ports around Britain

New York, USA

Words to help you...

food   Bedouin   Mountains   soil   resources   Marshy
adapted   camels   sparse   difficult   terracing
small   steep   climate   growing   South America

8   Sparse Populations

- Places with few people (........................ populations) may have .... **environments,** .... **or few** ....

- Deserts.

- ....

- Very cold places.

- .... grounds.

9   Adaptation: The Andes

- Small groups of people have .... to live in such places.

- The **Andes in** ....: altitude is high, slopes are ...., ... is poor.

- The people there have used .... to make the best use of the land.

10   Adaptation: Arctic Circle

- The .... **tribes** live in the **Middle East.**

- They move from place to place so they can find ....

- They use .... to move around.

11   Adaptation: Desert

- Although the population of these places is ...., the **world population is huge** and **still** .... every day.

12   World Population

- About .... **million** babies are born each year!

- **Birth Rate** = the number of .... born per 1,000 people per year.

- .... is now almost **7.5 billion (7,500,000,000!).**

13   Death Rate

- About .... **million people** die each year.

- **Death Rate** = the number of people who die, per .... people per ....

14   Growing Fast

- The world population is growing fast.

- The ....
(1900s) saw a '.........................
....'

Words to help you...

drop   rapid   balance   population density
grows   1 sq km   decreases

15 Why has the Population Grown?

- .... in **death rate** led to .... **growth** in the number of people.

Less people are dying!

But now there are too many people!

16 A Balance

- Population growth depends on .... between birth rate and death rate.

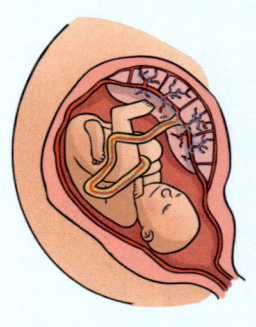

Birth Rate

Death Rate

17 Birth Rate vs Death Rate

- If the birth rate is **higher**, the population ....

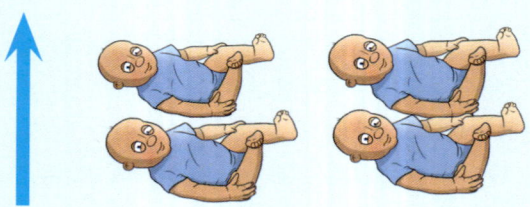

- If the death rate is **higher**, the population ....

18 ....

- .... measures **how many people** live in .... (average).

2 people

500 people

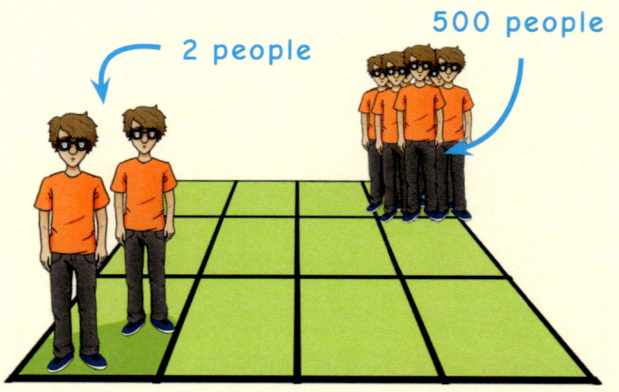

....

19   Distribution of People

• But, ... does **not** show how people are .... in that area (e.g. where they ......).

• 1 person may live in 1 street and .... may live 2 streets away!

20   The Right Number

• We need to have the .... **number** of people for the ....

• This is called ....

21   Over Population

What does 'over population' mean?

....
....
....

We are over populated!

22   Under Populated

What does 'under populated' mean?

....
....
....

Words to help you...

Pennines   mountains   988   Highlands   tourism   262   10

jobs   5,200   transport links   8   Snowdonia   difficult

23 **Density Around the World**

An area with **high population density** is Bangladesh; .... people per sq km

- The UK is .... per sq km

- Russia is only .... per sq km.

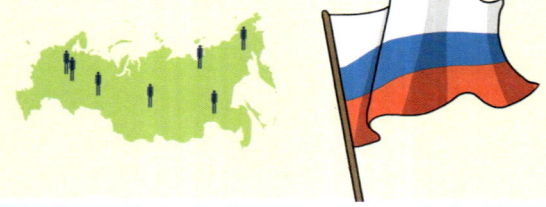

24 **Dense Populations (150+ people per square km)**

- In **London**, there are .... people per sq km.

- **Why do cities attract more people?**
  - ....
  - ....
  - ....

25 **Hills + Mountains**

- In the .... **of Scotland**, there are .... **per sq km**.

- There are steep hills and ....

26 **Sparse Populations (0-10 people per sq km)**

- The .... **and** .... have sparse populations.

- Why? ....
  ....

Words to help you...

Leeds   Germany   land   London   3rd   South
transport links   migrate   Industrial Revolution   France
Trading   63 million   wool trade

27   UK Cities

In cities, such as ....,
................, Manchester and Cardiff
the population is **dense**.

When did they start to grow?
....
....

· Why did these cities grow?
....
....
....

28   Southern England

· In the ...., growth has been more recent.

· There are **good** ....
.... for trade (Europe).

· People move to the UK
(.......................) from Europe.

29   UK & Europe

· The UK has the .... **highest** population in Europe
(.............................).

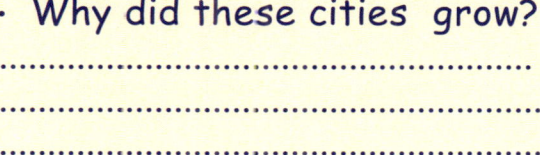

· .... and ....
are higher BUT they have much **more** ....

30   Overcrowding

- Give an example of an over crowded city ....
  in ....

- What is its population density?
  ....

....

31   Empty Land

- Why is high density in a city and a sparse population in the countryside not good?

....

32   2 Patterns Can Be Seen...

1. Where do populations tend to grow? ....
2. What are the two groups of countries seeing population growth?

- .... **nations** in .... and ....

- ...., **wealthy nations** such as Western .... and North .... (See pages 1 & 2)

developed   developing   ....

33   **High Death Rate**

- Why do some **developing** nations have a **high death** rate?

....
....
....

34   **High Birth Rate**

- Why might they also have a **high birth rate?**

....
....
....

35   **Migration (my-gray-shun)**

- What does migration mean?

....
....

Where are we currently seeing large numbers of migrants?

....

Welcome to ENGLAND

36   **Fewer Children**

- If people chose to have fewer children, how will this affect population growth?

....
....

37 Indonesia

In .... countries there has been a **big** population ....:

• Indonesia's population grew from .... **million** (1961) to .... **million** in 2011.

• That's a .... increase in 54 years.

.... increase in 49 years

38 India

• India; population grew from .... million (1952) to .... billion (2011).

• Increase of .... in 64 years

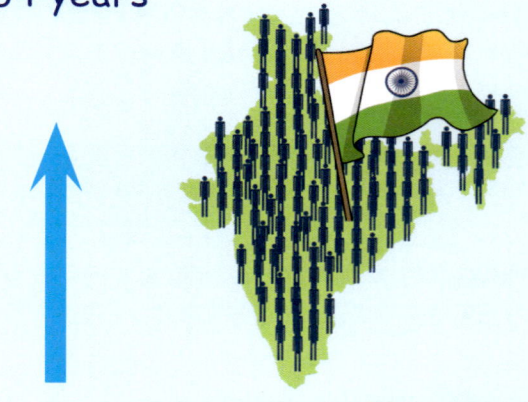

.... increase in 60 years

39 How fast is the Population Growing?

The United Nations reports:

World population is currently growing at around .... people per year.

.... per year!

40 More Growth

• Nearly **all** growth is in .... areas. This may rise from .... today to 7.8 billion in 2050.

• Population of **more developed** areas will remain **almost the same** (.......... billion).

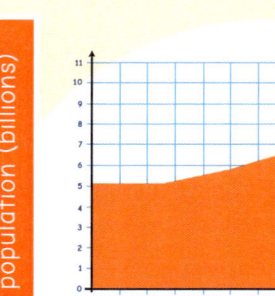

41   Over Population

- Not enough food in an area can lead to ....

- This can then cause ....

42   Control

Some governments, like ...., have taken action to .... population growth.

We must take action!

43   China's '.... .... per couple' policy

China has a '..... ....'.

There are **good** and **bad** things about this rule.

Only .... per couple!

This did control the .... **but** they will have too many .... people.

- Lots of people only wanted ....

- They .... **pregnancies** with girl babies.

- This means there will not be **enough** .... in China. in years to come.

This booklet is not to be photocopied. Thank you.

13

44   Demand for ....

- **More people** means **more** .... for energy.

- .... **countries** are increasing the use of .... **energy**.

45   Saving Our Resources

- Newly .... get most power from .... **fuels**.

- .... for energy is bigger than ever.

46   World Population Since 1200

- Colour the population growth in LEDCs in orange and MEDCs in green.

Key

☐ Developing Countries

☐ Developed Countries

WORLD POPULATION (millions)

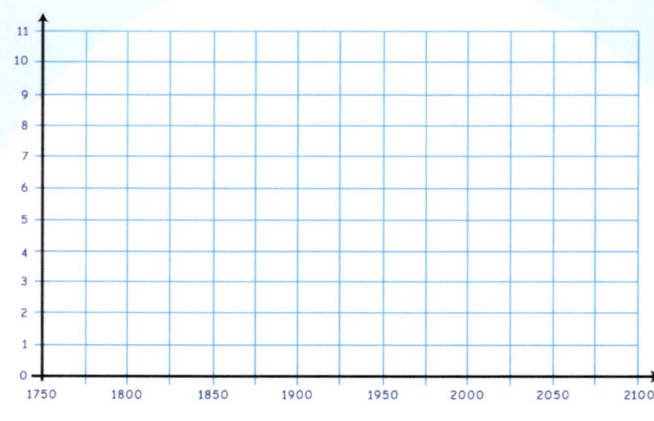

YEAR

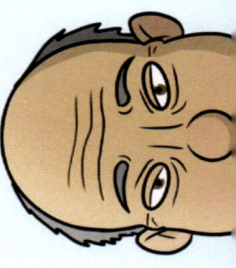

 **Population Pyramid (Kenya 2011)**

Population pyramids are graphs that show population **structure** (how a population is made up).

- Complete this graph for Kenya.

- What does this graph tell you about the population?

....
....
....
....
....

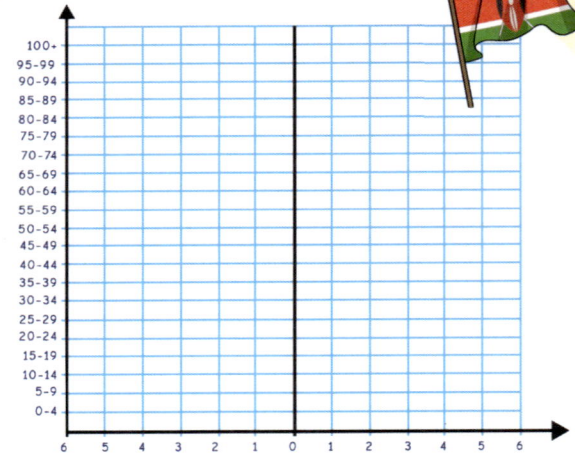

AGE

POPULATION (millions)

Key Male  Female

 **Population Pyramid (Japan 2011)**

The pyramid for Japan is a different shape. It does **not** look like a pyramid.

- Complete this graph for **Japan**.

- What does this graph tell you about the population.?

....
....
....
....
....

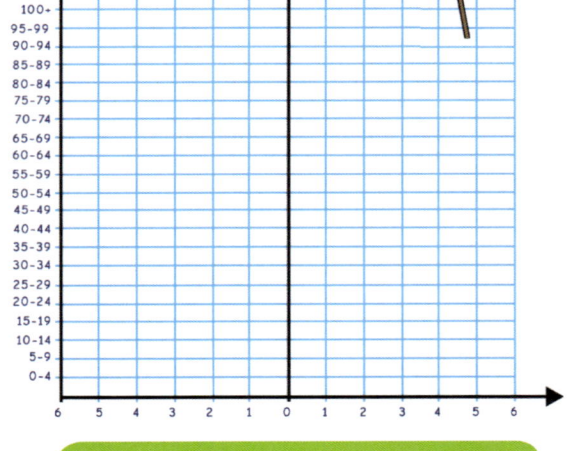

AGE

POPULATION (millions)

Key Male Female